To David

from Dad & Mummy

Christmas 1959.

THE CAMBRIDGE
CAROL-BOOK

BEING FIFTY-TWO SONGS FOR CHRISTMAS,
EASTER, AND OTHER SEASONS

EDITED BY

CHARLES WOOD

AND

GEORGE RATCLIFFE WOODWARD

LONDON

S·P·C·K

1957

First Published, 1924

Printed in Great Britain

CONTENTS

Christmas=Tide

Christmas=tide

I. ALTHOUGH AT YULE IT BLOWETH COOL

Words by G. R. W. Tune, *Der wind der wet, der han der kret* (1554), harmonized
for two voices by C. W.

1. Al-though at Yule it blow-eth cool, And frost doth grip the fin - gers, And

nip the nose, and numb the toes, Of out - door Car - ol sing - ers,

2. Through snow or sleet we pace the
street,
Fair sirs, with right good reason,
To wish you all, both great and
small,
The blessings of the season.

3. We think to spell 'Good news,
Nowell,
And eke a wonder story :
The Virgin mild hath borne the
Child :
E'en God, the King of Glory.'

4. We come to tell how once, o'er dell
And down, in winter-weather,
Led with a star, from lands afar
There rid three kings together.

5. By thoroughfare, through slum or
square,
Our Quire the praise rehearses
(As on we pass) of 'Wenceslas '
That 'Good King,' and his mercies.

6. Then we can sing, a pretty thing,
' The Holly and Ivy berry ;'
But best we ken 'Good gentle men,
God rest you, rest you merry.'

7. ' This hind'rest night I saw a sight:'
' A Virgin all unspotted,'
Ne'er be these lays of olden days
Out of remembrance blotted.

8. So 'Blessed be that Maid Marie,'
To spurn it 'twere a pity ;
Nor let men scorn 'A Babe is born
In Bethlem,' David city.

9. [No itching palms have we for
alms,
Content if Christ, the burden
Of these our lays, bestow His
praise,
And one day be our guerdon.

10. That hallow'd dome, Saint Dun-
stan's Home,
Doth harbour many blind folk,
To whom we pay the coin that
may
Be handed us by kind folk.]

11. The strain, yclept ' While shep-
herds kept,'
This also might be sung ye ;
But here an end. Us Christ defend,
And alway be among ye !

II. AS I WENT TO BETHLEHEM

Words by G. R. W.   A free translation of *Quem vidistis, pastores* (an Antiphon at Lauds, etc., on Christmas Day).   Tune, *As I went to Walsingham* (fourteenth or fifteenth century), harmonized by C. W.

1. As I went to Beth - le - hem, Ere the dawn of day,
2. *Quem vi - di - stis, pa - sto - res?* Tell me ev' - - ry whit:
3. New - ly born we saw the Babe, Whom an An - - gel throng

Met I with a knot of shep - herd men On their home-ward way.
In ter-ris (I fain would learn of ye) *Quis ap - pa - ru - it?*
Worshipt as the Lord; *Al - le - lu - ya, Glo - ri - a,* their song.

III. AWAKE, AND HEAR MY STORY

Words by G. R. W.   Setting from B. Gesius (1605), as given by Layriz.

1. A - wake, and hear my sto - ry! When God on Christ - mas
    Th' e - ter - nal Lord of glo - ry, Of Ma - ry Maid was

morn,
born. Seek-ing the King of a - ges, There journey'd from a -

far Three king - ly East - ern Sa - ges, By leng - thy dai - ly

sta - - - ges, Led west - ward by a Star.

2. The Star, it stood and pointed
   Toward the stable bare,
   Wherein the Lord's Anointed
   And eke His Mother were.
   Opening each his coffer,
   Balthàzar giveth myrrh ;
   While Melchïör doth offer
   Gold-ore ; see Gaspar proffer
   Incense, the gum of fir.

3. So go we and adore Him,
   Who was or time began :
   So worship we afore Him,
   Who stoops to die for man.
   Welcome we too that Mother,
   Thou Cherub higher, blest
   As woman ne'er was other,
   Who made the Lord our Brother,
   And rock'd her God to rest.

IV. BABE JESU, HEAR OUR DITTY

Words by G. R. W. Tune, *Le teint de son visage,* from Christophe Ballard's
Chansons à danser (1703), harmonized by G. R. W.

Ba - be Je - su, hear our dit - ty, And think there - of no

scorn: We pray Thee of Thy pi - ty, On this Thy na - tal

morn: We flee to Thee, Who wast, in Beth - lem

Ci - ty, Of Ma - ry Maid - en born For such as we.

V. BEHOULDE A SELY TENDER BABE
Or, NEW PRINCE, NEW POMPE

Words by Robert Southwell (1560-1593). Tune, *We are poor frozen-out gardeners,*
from W. Chappell's *Popular Music of the Olden Time,* p. 747, harmonized by C W.

2. Despise not Him for lying there,
  First what He is enquire :
  An orient perle is often found
  In depth of dirty mire.
Waye not His cribbe, His wodden dishe,
  Nor beastes that by Him feede :
Waye not His Mother's poore attire,
  Nor Josephe's simple weede.

3. This stable is a Prince's courte,
  The cribbe His chaire of state :
The beastes are parcell of His pompe,
  The wodden dishe His plate.

The parsons in that poor attire
  His royall liveries weare :
The Prince Himself is come from heaven,
  This pompe is prisèd there.

4. With joye approch, O Christen wighte,
  Do homage to thy Kinge:
And highly prise this humble pompe,
  Which He from heaven doth bring :
With joye approch, O Christen wighte,
  Do homage to thy Kinge :
And highly prise this humble pompe
  Which He from heaven doth bringe.

VI. BLEST, WITHOUTEN MATCH

Words by G. R. W. Tune, *Branle de la torche*, from Thoinot Arbeau's *Orchésographie* (1588), harmonized by G.R.W.

1. Blest, withouten match,
   O Bethlem, is the gable
   O'er that lowly cratch:—
   The crib within thy stable.
   For, as Babe, therein
   That Lord and God abideth,
   Who on Cherubyn
   Aloft in glory rideth.   Alleluia.

2. He is born to shrive
   The son, his goods who squander'd,
   Born to save alive
   The sheep, that far had wander'd.
   So bear we in mind
   To hymn this heavenly stranger : —
   God, who, for mankind,
   Did not abhor the manger.   Alleluia.

VII. CHRIST IS AT THY PORTALS

Words, ’Εγγίζει ὁ Χριστὸς (December 20), by St. Romanos the Melodist (*c.* 496), translated by G. R. W.   Tune, *Air de la Gavote*, from Thoinot Arbeau's *Orchésographie*, harmonized by G. R. W.

Call the king - ly stran - - - ger Out of Per - sian land.
Thus, and in due or - - - - der, Hosts An - ge - lick sing.

VIII. DING DONG! MERRILY ON HIGH

Words by G. R. W. Tune, *Branle de l'Official*, from Thoinot Arbeau's *Orchésographie*, (1588), harmonized by C. W.

1. Ding dong! mer-ri-ly on high   in heav'n the bells are ring - ing:
   Ding dong! ver-i-ly the sky   is riv'n with An-gel sing - ing.
2. E'en so here be-low, be-low,   let stee-ple bells be swung - en,
   And i - o, i-o, i - o,   by priest and peo-ple sung - en.
3. Pray you, du-ti-ful-ly prime   your Mat-in chime, ye ring - ers;
   May you beau-ti-ful-ly rime   your Eve-time Song, ye sing - ers:

Glo - ri-a, Ho - san - na in ex - cel - sis!

IX. FROM GALILEE THEY CAME

Words by G. R. W. Tune, *Ah! mon beau laboureur*, of the sixteenth century, harmonized by G. R. W.

1. From Ga - li - lee they came, Saint Jo - seph and his Dame: O'er hill they speed, nor dal - ly up val - ley, up val - ley: O'er hill they speed, nor dal - ly up val-ley, O la!

2. When night fell dark and chill,
   And wind 'gan whistle shrill,
Went Joseph and his Dearie, aweary, aweary,
Went Joseph and his Dearie, aweary, O la!

3. Arriv'd in Bethlehem,
   There was but found for them
(The best that they were able) a stable, a stable,
('Twas all that they were able) a stable, O la!

X. GET IVY AND HULL, WOMAN, DECK UP

Words by Thomas Tusser (*c.* 1523–1580). Tune, *Bannocks o' barley meal*, harmonized by C. W.

1. Get i - vy and hull, wo-man, deck up thine house, And take this same brawn for to
Pro - vide us good cheer, for thou know'st the old guise; Old cus-toms, that good be, let

seethe and to souse; At Christ-mas be mer - ry, and thank God of all, And
no man de - spise.

feast thy poor neighbours, the great and the small: Yea, all the year long have an

eye to the poor, And God shall send luck to keep o - pen thy door.

2. Good fruit and good plenty do well in thy loft,
Then lay for an orchard and cherish it oft.
The profit is mickle, the pleasure is much;
At pleasure with profit few wise men will grutch.

At Christmas be merry, and thank God of all,
And feast thy poor neighbours, the great and the small:
Yea, all the year long have an eye to the poor,
And God shall send luck to keep open thy door.

XI. HAIL! ETERNAL SON, TO THEE

Words by G. R. W.   Melody of *Gregis pastor Tityrus*, from a Mosburg Gradual (A.D. 1360), harmonized by G. R. W.

1. Hail! E-ter-nal Son, to-day Born of Ma-ry, Maid-en . . ay; Straw Thy bed, Thy pil-low hay. E-ya, e-ya, e-ya; *Do-mi-ni na-ta-li-a re-col-at ec-cle-si-a.*

2. Angel-army, sound your horn,
Chanting on this holy morn,
' God in Bethlehem is born.'
   Eya, eya, eya ;
   In excelsis gloria :
   In terris concordia.

3. Shine in Eastern sky, thou Star,
Pointing to that house afar,
Wherein Babe and Mother are.
   Eya, eya, eya ;
   Puer idem varia
   Fecit luminaria.

4. Hitherward ! Ye Princes three,
Worship Him.   Though poor He be,
Lord, and King of kings is He.
   Eya, eya, eya ;
   In celesti patria
   Vestra sors palacia.

5. Herdmen, leave your flocks, and run
To adore the Holy One,
God, the Father's only Son.
   Eya, eya, eya ;
   Qui creavit omnia,
   Eius haec solempnia.

6. Ass, with ox that hauleth plow,
Fore thy Master, cradled now
In the manger, bend and bow.
   Eya, eya, eya ;
   Inter animalia
   Patrem parit filia

7. Joseph, many of high degree,
King and Seer, have long'd to see
Whom thou seest on Mary's knee.
   Eya, eya, eya ;
   Deus, tuos visita,
   Et nobiscum habita.

8. Now, good people, all of ye,
Magnify, with Maid Marie,
Christ and His Nativitie.
   Eya, eya, eya ;
   Sociate musicâ
   Christi Natalitia.

XII. HAIL! HOLY CHILD, LAIN IN AN OXEN MANGER

Words by G. R. W.   Tune, *Quittez, pasteurs, vos brebis et houlette,* an old Flemish air, harmonized by C. W.

1. Hail! Ho - ly Child, Lain in an ox - en man - ger, Of Jes - se stem, Yet
2. Me - think I stand To - day in Da-vid's Ci - ty, And twang the chord For
3. What if my flute Break time with An-gel sing - ers, Or not sur - pass The
4. Thou wilt ac - cept My song, nor re-pre-hend it : For Thee, a - bove All

scorn'd at Beth - le - hem, In win - ter wild, As ne'er - to - fore was
Da - vid's Son and Lord : If, harp in hand, I make but tune - less
Al - to of yon ass; If, What if my lute Be pluck'd with art - less
earth - ly things, I love : And, tho' in - - ept my lay, Thou wilt a -

stran - ger, Constrain'd, as I hear tell, Out - side, out - side a chur-lish
dit - ty, Yet, Babe, Thou know'st that I As - say, as - say my best—a
fin - gers, Or if my voice be Base, Now flat, now flat, now sharp, be-
mend it, And where 'tis out of joint, Canst make, canst make my false true

inn to dwell, Out - side, out - side a chur - lish inn to dwell.
lul - la - by, As - say, as - say my best—a lul - la - by.
reft of grace, Now flat, now flat, now sharp, be - reft of grace—
count - er - point, canst make, canst make my false true count - er - point.

XIII. HEAP ON MORE WOOD! THE WIND IS CHILL

Words by Sir Walter Scott (1771–1832)   Tune, *Corn rigs*, harmonized by C.W.

1. Heap on more wood! the wind is chill; But let it whis - tle

as it will, We'll keep our Christ-mas mer - ry still, We'll

keep our Christ - mas mer - ry still. Each age has deem'd the

new-born year The fit - test time for fes - tal cheer; And well our Christ-ian

sires   of   old   I ov'd when the year its course had roll'd.

2. On Christmas Eve the bells were rung ;
   On Christmas Eve the Mass was sung ;
   That only night in all the year
   Saw the stoled priest the chalice rear.
   The damsel donn'd her kirtle sheen ;
   The hall was dress'd with holly green ;
   Forth to the wood did merry men go
   To gather in the mistletoe.

3. Then open'd wide the baron's hall
   To vassal, tenant, serf and all ;
   Power laid his rod of rule aside,
   And ceremony doff'd his pride.
   All hail'd, with uncontroll'd delight
   And general voice, the happy night,
   That to the cottage, as the crown,
   Brought tidings of salvation down.

4. The fire, with well-dried logs supplied,
   Went roaring up the chimney wide ;
   The huge hall-table's oaken face,
   Scrubb'd till it shone, the day to grace,
   Bore then upon its massive board
   No mark to part the squire and lord.
   Then the grim boar's head frown'd on high,
   Crested with bays and rosemary.

5. The wassel round, in good brown bowls,
   Garnish'd with ribbons, blithely trowls ;
   There the huge sirloin reek'd ; hard by
   Plum-porridge stood, and Christmas pie.
   Then came the merry masquers in,
   And carols roar'd with blithesome din :
   If unmelodious was the song,
   It was a hearty note and strong.

6. England was Merry England, when
   Old Christmas brought his sports agen :
   'Twas Christmas broach'd the mightiest ale :
   'Twas Christmas told the merriest tale ;
   A Christmas gambol oft would cheer
   The poor man's heart through half the year.
   England was Merry England, when
   Old Christmas brought his sports agen.

XIV. HO! STEWARD, BID MY SERVANTS

Words by J. M. Neale (1818–1866), reverently altered here and there to suit an ancient ecclesiastical pre-Reformation melody, now known as *John Anderson, my jo, John.* Here it is harmonized by C. W.

1. 'Ho! steward, bid my ser - vants Go forth, and hi - ther call, For guests, my friends and neigh - bours, To sup with me in hall; That, at this bless - ed sea - son, Which comes but once a year, We may, as folk in old - en days, Re - joice, and make good cheer.'

2. 'Sire, shall I bid the noble,
   That banquets in his state,
   With purple and fine linen,
   With gold and silver plate ?'
   'Nay, bid me not the noble,
   For he hath got enow;
   But bring me in the country man,
   That liveth by the plow.'

3. 'Sire, shall I bid in Divès,
   For it is very plain,
   If ye give him a banquet,
   He'll banquet you again ?'
   'Nay, bid not hither Divès,
   For it shall ne'er be thus,
   But go among the alley-lanes,
   And fetch in Lazarus.'

4. 'Sire, shall I bid the merchant,
   That hath upon the seas
   His fleets of caravellas,
   And right great argosies ?'
   'Nay, bid me not the merchant,
   But go and fetch the clerk,
   That with the bandog goes to rest,
   And riseth with the lark.'

5. 'And wherefore must I turn me
   From noble and from rich ?
   And wherefore seek the poor man,
   That dwells in lane and ditch ?'
   'Man, lay to heart the reason,
   Because the King of all,
   Though rich, grew poor, for mortal sake.
   And born was in a stall.

5. 'For these be they, good steward,
   Whom God doth chiefly choose,
   And these, His poorer brethren,
   No man may dare refuse.
   So, in this bleak December,
   Then make we best good cheer,
   When, for the sake of Babe Jesú,
   The poor we welcome here.'

XV. HOB AND COLIN, YULE IS COME

The words, by G. R. W., are founded on those of *Guillô, pran ton tamborin,* a
Burgundian carol (1720): set to its proper melody by C. W.

1. Hob and Co-lin, Yule is come, Calling forth your fife and drum; If ye
strike up, as ye can, Tú-re-lú-re-lú, pá-ta-pá-ta-pán, I will
ca-rol; so will Jan With a las-sie, Joan or Nan.

2. Thus men gave, in olden days,
   To the Prince of princes, praise:
   Wherefore, an ye like my plan,
   Turelurelu, patapatapan,
   Dress your drum-stick, you; and
   span,
   You, your reed, my piper Pan.

3. Christmas tolls the devil's knell;
   Thankèd be Emmanuel.
   So, from England to Japan,
   Turelurelu, patapatapan,
   Whether town or country
   man,
   Sing it, ring it, ran-tan-ran.

4. God and man accordant are:
   Not so, fife and drum; ye jar.
   Yet nought would I sooner thar.
   Turelurelu, patapatapan.
   Fore our Lady and Saint Ann,
   'Tis high time the thing began.

XVI. IN A CAVERN OXEN-TROD

Words of Σπηλαίῳ παρῴκησας (December 25), by St. Anatolius († 458), translated by G. R. W., and set to the tune of *Een Soudaen had een Dochterken* by J. R. Lunn, B.D.

1. In a ca-vern ox - en-trod, Je - su Christ, Thou li - est,

In a man-ger, ve - ry God, Thou, the Son most high - est.

2. There poor herdmen from the fold
   Bend the knee before Thee :
   There with incense, myrrh and gold,
   Eastern kings adore Thee.

3. Now at length is come to pass
   That which had been tolden,
   Touching Christ and Christen-mas,
   By the prophets olden.

4. Now Angelick hosts aloft
   Cleave the sky asunder,
   Carolling, in loud and soft,
   Songs of glee and wonder.

5. 'Glory be to God,' they cry,
   'God, who condescendest
   To be born ; who from on high
   Man alone befriendest.'

XVII. IN BETHLEHEM HEAR I TO-DAY

Words of Δόξα ἐν ὑψίστοις Θεῷ (December 25) by St. John Damascene († *c.* 780), translated by G. R. W.   Tune from H. v. Loufenberg's Geistliche Lieder, *Ich wollt dasz ich daheime wär* (*c.* 1420), harmonized by C. W.

In Beth-le-hem hear I to-day The An-gels chant a mer-ry lay.

2. And ' Glory be to God on high,
   That willeth Peace on earth,' they cry.

3. Now doth the Mother-maid enfold
   Him whom high heav'n can no-way hold.

4. 'Mid darkness hath the Day-star shined,
   Exalting men of humble mind,

5. Who, with the Angels in the sky,
   Sing, ' Glory be to God on high !'

Another setting of the above : this also by C W.

In Beth-le-hem hear I to-day The An-gels chant a mer-ry lay.

XVIII. LET SUCH (SO FANTASTICAL) LIKING NOT THIS

Words by Thomas Tusser (*c.* 1523-80), set to an old English melody by C. W.

1. Let such (so fan - tas - tic - al) lik - ing not this,
Nor a - ny thing hon - est that an - ci - ent is,

Give place to the time, that so meet we do

see, Ap - point - ed of God, as it seem-eth to be.

2. At Christmas, good husbands have corn in the ground,
   In barn, and in cellar, worth many a pound,
   Things plenty in house (beside cattle and sheep),
   All sent them (no doubt on) good houses to keep.

3. At Christmas, the hardness of winter doth rage,
   A griper of all things, especially age ;
   Then likely poor people, the young with the old
   Be sorest oppressèd with hunger and cold.

4. At Christmas, by labour is little to get ;
   That wanting, the poorest in danger are set :
   What season, then, better of all the whole year,
   Thy needy poor neighbour to comfort and cheer ?

XIX. THIS HAPPY MORN THE MAID HATH BORNE

Words by G. R. W. for the tune (in the Phrygian Mode) of *Maria zart, von edler Art.*
The setting thereof is by Michael Praetorius (1610).

1. This hap - py morn The Maid hath borne The Lord of bliss e-
2. With tri - ple gift Three kings full swift Are hast - ing to a-

tern - al: That God, who wrought All things from nought, Ter - res - tri -
dore him: Where star-light shone, It led them on To kneel in

al, su - per - nal: Tho' earth but gave This Babe a cave
faith a - fore him. Next, on the lea Some herd-men see,

To be, at birth, His dwell - - - ing, The heav'nly star is
More sheen than light of thun - - - der, A great and migh - ty

tell - - - - - ing
won - - - - - der;

To peo - ple yet In
When from the sky An

dark - ness set
An - gel high

Of Je - sus Christ,
De - clar'd the birth

The Lord most high'st,
Of God on earth;

The Sun that set - teth ne - - - ver.
The wel-come Gos - pel sto - - - ry.

The same, I say,
Then hosts a - loft

Both yes - ter - day,
Sang loud and soft:

Now this day, and for - e - - - ver.
'To God on high be glo - - - ry!'

XX. MY LORD, AND MY GOD, IN BETHLEHEM BORN

Words by G. R. W.   Tune, *O Jesulein süsz, O Jesulein mild :* melody and harmony
by Samuel Scheidt (1585-1650).

1. My Lord, and my God, in Beth-le-hem born, Sweet Babe Je-su, on Christ-mas morn: Hail! E - - ver-last-ing Son, dis-play'd To mor-tal view by Ma - - ry Maid, My Lord, and my God, in Beth-le-hem born.

2. More wonderful sight hath **n**ever bin seen ;
For Thou, in stable bare and mean,
Though King of heav'n, art fain to rest
Upon an earthly mother's breast :
More wonderful sight ne'er, ne'er shall
be seen.

3. Thou in the beginning madest the skies,
Bespangling heav'n with stars for eyes :
And Thou didst form this earth of ours,
Adorning it with trees and flow'rs ;
Yet swath'd in a crib their Fashioner
lies.

4. Around the dry land Thou pouredst the sea,
And set'st his bounds with sure decree ·
But, bending heaven, so to crown
Mankind with bliss, Thou camest down :
Babe Jesu, my God, all glory to Thee !

XXI. NOW STAND WE IN THE VILLAGE

Words by G. R. W. Tune, *Khanta zagun guziek* (a Basque air), harmonized by G. R. W.

1. 'Now stand we in the vil - - lage, Where Jes - se's bairns were born;
A - mid the fields of til - - lage, Whence Bo - az reap'd his corn.
Here wel - leth Da - vid's Fountain; There Ra - chel's bo - dy
lies: Soon o'er yon East - ern moun - tain Shall Ja-cob's Star a - rise.

2. 'The seventy weeks, appointed
    Of God, are now fulfill'd :
Ere long the Lord's Anointed
    Shall born be, as He will'd ;
Whereat the prophet wond'red
    When Gabriel told him so
In Babylon, four hundred
    And thirty years ago.

3. 'Which Gabriel late did meet thee,
    And, with divining rod,
Right reverently greet thee
    As Mother to his God.
Let Ahaz read his dial,
    And (e'en as Esay bade)
Confess, without denial,
    The Son of Mary Maid.

4. 'Now, Lady, 'mid the number
    Of pilgrim folk, our kin,
Go seek we place of slumber,
    And shelter 'neath yond inn '
'Good Joseph, 'neath that gable
    In chamber, great or small,
The host will not be able
    To find us room withal :

5. 'So turn we from the tavei_
    And, seeing night is nigh,
Seek lodging in this cavern,
    Where kine and assen lie.'
Ah ! Bethlem, didst thou know it,
    Of yonder Maid, e'er morn,
As Micah did foreshow it,
    In thee shall God be born.

XXII. O THE MORN, THE MERRY MERRY MORN

Words by G. R. W. Tune, *O the broom, the bonny bonny broom* (sixteenth or seventeenth century), harmonized by C. W.

1. O the morn, the merry merry morn, The morn of Christmas - Day, When God, the Son of God was born Of Ma - ry maiden ay!

2. Sweet the song, the happy happy song,
    Precented at His birth,
And caught up by the heav'nly throng,
    ' Good-will, and Peace on earth ! '

3. To the town, the tiny tiny town,
    The town of Bethlem, ran
Some simple shepherds, o'er the down,
    To view Him God and Man.

4. There within a cattle cattle shed
    They find and worship Him,
Who rideth, in His realm o'erhead,
    Upon the Cherubim.

5. So, my boys, my bonny bonny boys,
    To Bethlem off be we !
But, pray you, shun whate'er annoys
    The Babe on Mary's knee.

XXIII. OUR LADY SAT WITHIN HER BOWER

Words by G. R. W.   **Tune, in the Phrygian Mode (from Hayn v. Themar'**
Lieder, 1590), harmonized by C. W

1. Our La - dy sat with - in her bow'r, And sweet - ly sang from hour to hour, La-lul-la - lu : Ho! rest thee, my Bairn, and my God there-to ; La - lul - la, Babe Je - su . . . . !

2. In reverent wise, with holy hands,
   She wrapt the Child in swathing bands.

3. But, as she sung the glad refrain,
   Her tears gan trickle fast as rain.

4. A wonder sight it was to see
   How Mary rockt Him on her knee,

5. And bade Him rest, and stint His weep,
   Who giveth His belovèd sleep.

XXIV. OUTSIDE, HOW HARD IT BLOWETH!

Words by G. R. W.   Tune (*Ich will bei meinem Leben*) and setting by H. Schütz (1585-1672).

1. Out - side, how hard it blow - eth, The nor' - nor' - east - ern gale!
   Out - side, how fast it snow - eth! 'Twill freeze the milk in pail.
   Ay me! how dark the night! Nay, e'en when day do length-en,
   (Men say) the cold will streng - then, Ere sum - mer draw
   in sight, . . . Ere sum - mer draw in sight.

2. Indoors, meanwhile 'tis merry:
     Men trim the house with spray
   Of rud red holly berry.
     Or green-leaf of the bay.
   To curb the winter cold,
     The spit is set a-turning;
     The Yule block too is burning,
   As in the days of old.

3. In hall, despite the weather,
     Good will and warmth abound:
   There hearts are knit together
     With Carol, Glee and Round,
   In worship of that morn,
     When God was [in December,
     As grateful folk remember]
   Of Maiden Mary born.

XXV. PAST THREE A CLOCK, AND A COLD FROSTY MORNING

The refrain, *Past three a clock*, is old, but the rest of the Carol is newly composed by G. R. W. The tune (*London Waits*, from W. Chappell's *Popular Music of the Olden Time*, p. 550) is here harmonized by C. W.

℟. Past three a clock, And a cold fro‑sty morn‑ing: Past three a clock; Good mor‑row, mas‑ters all! 1. ℣. Born is a Ba — — by, Gen‑tle as máy be, Son of th' e‑ter‑nal Fa‑ther su‑per‑nal. ℟. Past three a clock, etc.

2. ℣. Seraph quire singeth,
Angel bell ringeth:
Hark how they rime it,
Time it, and chime it. ℟.

3. ℣. Mid earth rejoices
Hearing such voices
Ne'ertofore só well
Carolling *Nowell*. ℟.

4. ℣. Hinds o'er the pearly
Dewy lawn early
Seek the high stranger
Laid in the manger. ℟.

5. ℣. Cheese from the dairy
Bring they for Mary,
And, not for money,
Butter and honey. ℟.

6. ℣. Light out of star‑land
Leadeth from far land
Princes, to meet him,
Worship and greet him. ℟.

7. ℣. Myrrh from full coffer,
Incense they offer:
Nor is the golden
Nugget withholden. ℟.

8. ℣. Thus they: I pray you,
Up, sirs, nor stay you
Till ye confess him
Likewise, and bless him. ℟.

XXVI. SLEEP, BABY MINE, IN HAPPY CASE

Words by G. R. W.   Tune and setting of *Es war einmal ein reicher man* (Eisleben, 1598).

1. Sleep, ba - by mine, in hap - - py case: Thy guardian
   To whom the dark-ness and the light Co - - e - qual
2. But hard - er was the plank, where - on The Suff'rer
   Of leo - pard, bear, wolf, li - - on, snake. Him sing I,

ey - eth, face to face, Our heav'n - ly Fa - ther e - - ver,
are: who, day and night thy keep - er, slumb'reth ne - - ver.
mount - ed, woe - be - gone, To save thy life from dan - ger.
babe, Who for our sake Did not ab - hor the man - ger.

1. Yet know, thou child in rich ar - ray, On fea - ther bed,
2. What time the Vir - gin - Mo - ther kept The cratch, where-in

that on a day Thy Ma - ker couch'd in straw and hay.
her Dar-ling slept, Or oft, as Man of Sor - row, wept.

XXVII. SWEET BABE, THAT, WRAPT IN TWILIGHT SHADE

Words by W. J. Blew (1808–1894). Melody and setting of *Hats Gott versehn* by Balthasar Musculus (1597).

1. Sweet Babe, that, wrapt in twi - light shade, Up - on Thy
Mo - ther's lap wast laid, Grant, Ho - ly Je - su, grant that we
May i - mi - tate Thine in - - fan - - cy.

2. And, when we seek our lowly bed,
   While midnight darkens o'er our head,
   From ravening wolves, kind Shepherd, keep
   This little flock of Thy poor sheep.

3. Speak peace unto our souls, and tell
   Of heav'nly joys with Thee that dwell;
   So shall our spirit, all night long,
   Sing to our God her thankful song.

4. Thus, as the dying day grows dim,
   To God we raise our evening hymn;
   And laud, with heaven's bright Angel host,
   The Father, Son and Holy Ghost.

XXVIII. THE MIRROUR OF THE FATHER'S FACE

Words by G. R. W.   Set to the tune of *En Trinitatis speculum* by C. W.

1. The Mir-rour of the Fa-ther's face Dark-ness from the world gan chase, When, as mor-tal vest - ed, God was ma-ni-fest - ed. Wherefore, Chris - tens, up and sing To Je - sus Christ, of hea - ven King. God is born, go meet Him, And with ca - rol greet Him . . .

2. The Maid hath borne the Holy One,
    God the Father's only Son,
    Of His great compassion,
    Found in human fashion.
Wherefore, Churchmen, sing for joy,
And, leal to Mary's gentle Boy,
    Keep His birth-day yearly,
    Loving Him sincerely.

3. He lieth in a crib of tree,
    Altogether lovely He :
    Holy, Strong, Immortal,
    Key to David's portal.
Wherefore, masters, be not sad,
When Christmas biddeth men be glad,
    But with voice canorous
    Swell the Seraph-chorus.

XXIX. TO REDEEM A RACE FORLORN

Words by G. R. W. Tune of *Anni novi novitas*, from a Mosburg Gradual (A.D. 1360), harmonized by C. W.

1. To re - deem a race for - lorn, When the nights were long - est,
2. 'Glo - ry be to God on high; And on earth be grant - ed

In the sign of Ca - pri - corn, When the frost is strong - est,
Peace, Good-will to men,' hear I O'er the wel - kin chant - ed.

Neath the ga - ble Of a sta - ble, Ear - ly on a morn,
Earth . . re - joices, Hear-ing voi - ces Arch - an - gel - ick sing

Of a low - ly Maid - en, Ho - ly Je - su, Thou wert born.
An - them sweet - est, As 'tis meet - est, To the new - born King.

XXX. TO BETHLEHEM THAT NIGHT *and* WITH STRANGE AND WONDROUS WAYS

Words of certain Troparia for Christmas, translated by G. R. W.   Set to the French Psalm XIX.   Harmonized by Anon.

'Εν Βηθλεὲμ συνέδραμον (December 26).

In - - car - nate there they find The Ma - ker

of man - kind: To Him be glo - ry gi - - ven!

'Εξαίσιον δρόμον (December 25)

2. With strange and wondrous ways
   The Magi saw the rays
       Of one new-lighted Star.
   Star heretofore so sheen
   Their eyes had never seen:
       It shone from heav'n afar,
   And signified the birth
   Of Christ a King on earth:
       And rightly so they reckon'd;
   To save mankind forlorn
   This royal Babe was born,
       Whose Star to Bethlem beckon'd.

Neηγενès (December 25).   The same, harmonized by C. Goudimel (✠ 1572).

3. 'The new - born Bairn, where may He be,
For hi - ther come are we, To bow

King He - rod, say, Whose com-et was a - glow:
to Him the knee.' This would the wise men know.

But He - rod, trou - bled sore, And Sa -

lem o - - ver - more, Was mind-ed in his fu - - ry

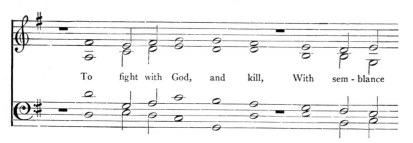

To fight with God, and kill, With sem - blance

of good - will, The In - fant King of Jew - - ry.

'Ηκρίβωσε χρόνον (December 25)

4. Then Herod straight would know
What time the star gan show
    That led the Princes three
To Bethlehem, that there
With giftès, rich and rare,
    The Babe might honour'd be.
But, by our Lord's command,
Safe in their native land
    By other road they find them.
Thus did the Kings deride
False Herod at that tide,
    And left him far behind them.

XXXI. TO US THIS MORN A CHILD IS BORN

Words by G. R. W. Tune, *Jog on, jog on the footpath way*, an Elizabethan melody in the Mixo-lydian mode, harmonized by C. W.

1. To us this morn a Child is born, His Father is none o - ther Than

God the King of ev' - ry thing, Maid Ma - ry is . . . His Mo - ther.

2. Her Babe is Lord by all adored ;
   Esaias had foreshown her :
   Now came't to pass that ox and ass
   Bow'd down afore their owner.

3. When Herod heard the Mages' word,
   He smote the babes asunder
   In all that coast, a blameless host,
   From two years old and under.

4. Now, faithful quire, bless God the Sire,
   Bless God the Spirit Holy,
   Bless God, the Son ere time begun,
   Now lain in manger lowly.

XXXII. 'TWAS IN A CAVE ON CHRISTMAS MORN

Words by G. R. W. Tune, *Dich grüssen wir, O Jesulein* (Constance, 1623), harmonized by C. W.

1. 'Twas in a cave on Christ-mas morn, No-well, No-well, Je-sus, the Son of God was born, No-well, No-well, No - well. . .

2. See in a crib the heav'nly Child,
   Lullay, Lulláy,
   Cradled by Mary, Maiden mild,
   La-Lullaby, Lúllay.

3. Thitherward kings and herdmen drew
   To Ephratá,
   For to adore the Babe Jesú,
   At Bethlem Ephráta.

4. Then was fulfill'd the thing foretold,
   Eya, Eyá,
   In holy writ by bards of old,
   Eya, Eya, Eya.

5. Armies Angelick sang for mirth
   Cum Maria,
   Marvellous glad o'er Jesu's birth
   Ex Matre María.

6. *Gloria tibi, Domine,*
   Alleluyá,
   Qui natus es pro homine,
   Alle-Allelúya.

XXXIII. WHEN ANGELICK HOST ENTUNED

Words by G. R. W. Tune, *Heinz, wiltu Christa han* (Frankfurt, 1582), harmonizeᴅ by G. R. W.

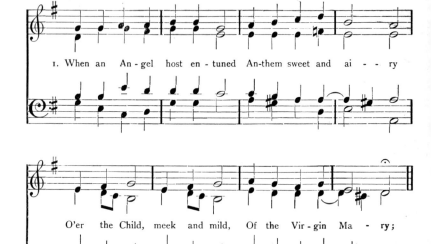

1. When an An - gel host en - tuned An-them sweet and ai - - ry

O'er the Child, meek and mild, Of the Vir - gin Ma - ry;

2. When, with honey, herd-men brought
    Butter from the dairy
  To the One Holy Son
    Born of Maiden Mary;

3. When iii pilgrim kings unlockt
    Each his casket, spary
  Of no thing for this King,
    God, the Son of Mary,

4. 'Glory be to God on high,
    God, who cannot vary!
  Was the lay on that day
    Sung by Blessèd Mary.

XXXIV. WHILE SHEPHERDS WATCH'D THEIR FLOCKS BY NIGHT

Words by N. Tate (1652–1715). Tune of *Lobt Gott, ihr Christen alle gleich*, by Nic. Herman (1560), harmonized by J. S. Bach (1685–1750).

1. While shep-herds watch'd their flocks by night, All seat-ed on the ground, The An - gel of the Lord came down, And glo - ry shone a - round, . . And glo - ry shone a - round.

2. 'Fear not,' said he (for mighty dread
   Had seized their troubled mind),
   'Glad tidings of great joy I bring
   To you and all mankind.

3. 'To you in David's town this day
   Is born of David's line
   A Saviour, who is Christ the Lord,
   And this shall be the sign :

4. 'The heav'nly Babe you there shall find
   To human view display'd,

   All meanly wrapt in swathing bands,
   And in a manger laid.'

5. Thus spake the Seraph ; and forth-with
   Appear'd a shining throng
   Of Angels praising God, and thus
   Addrest their joyful song :

6. 'All glory be to God on high,
   And to the earth be peace ;
   Good-will henceforth from heav'n to men
   Begin and never cease.'

New Year's Day, Lady Day and August 7

XXXV. JESUS IS THE SWEETEST NAME

Words by G. R. W. Set to their proper melody, *Jesus ist ein süsser Nam* (Munich, 1586), by C. W.

1. Je - sus is the sweet - est Name That heart can fan - cy,
2. On the eight day, when they came To give the heav'n-ly
3. Je - sus is the Name full well Be - dread - ed and ab -

tongue can frame; Re - veal'd to Ma - ry in her cell At
Child His Name, 'Let call Him Je - sus,' Ma - ry cried: 'A -
horr'd in hell; But Je - sus is the theme and boast Of

Na - - za - - reth by Ga - - bri - - el; Where -
men,' said Jo - - seph at that tide; 'Be -
Chris - tian men and An - - gel host. So

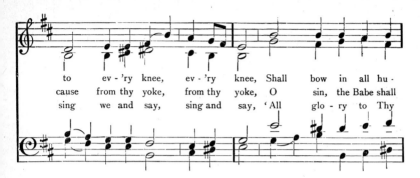

to   ev - 'ry   knee,   ev - 'ry   knee, Shall   bow   in   all   hu -
cause from thy yoke,   from thy yoke,   O   sin,   the Babe shall
sing   we and say,   sing and   say,   'All   glo - ry   to   Thy

mi - li - - ty.   .   .   .   .
save His   folk.'   .   .   .   .
Name to - - day!'   .   .   .   .

Fourth Sunday after Epiphany

XXXVI. WHEN CHRIST HAD (AS RECOUNTED)

The eighth chapter of St. Matthew (vv. 23-27) turned into English verse by G. R. W., and set by him to a Meistersinger Song of the sixteenth century, *Matthaeus schreibt am achten.* The melody lies in the tenor.

1. When Christ had (as re - count - ed In Mat - thew chap - ter eight)
   With His dis - ci - ples mount - ed The ship, 'twas wax - ing late:

Then rose the wind: the bil - low A - round the boat gan leap; But

He lay on a pil - - low A - board, a - baft, a - sleep. . . . .

2. 'Lord, save us ; else we perish,'
    His fellow shipmen spake :
   'No longer hope we cherish :
    Lord, from Thy slumber wake !'
   Said He, 'Why are ye fearful,
    O ye of little faith ?
   Take heart of grace ! Be cheer-
    ful !'
   Then He arose, and saith.

3. 'Be tranquil, O thou breaker !
    Thou whirlwind, be at rest !'
   The breezes knew their Maker :
    The waves, too, lower'd their
    crest.
   Then cried the men in wonder,
    'What manner man is He,
   Whose very word hath under
    Control both wind and sea ?'

Lady Day

XXXVII. THERE STOOD IN HEAVEN A LINDEN TREE
(*Es stot ein lind im himelrich*)

Words and tune (sixteenth or fifteenth century) from H. v. Loufenberg's *Geistliche Lieder, c.* 1420. The English translation by G. R. W. The melody harmonized by G. H. Palmer, Mus.Doc.

1. There stood in heav'n a lind-en tree; But, tho' 'twas ho-ney la - - den, All An-gels cried, 'No bloom shall be Like that of one fair Maid - en.'

The above, harmonized for two voices by C. W.

There stood in heav'n a lin-den tree, But, tho' 'twas ho-ney-la - - den, All An-gels cried, 'No bloom shall be Like that of one fair Maid - en.'

2. Sped Gabriel on wingèd feet,
   And pass'd through bolted portals
   In Nazareth, a Maid to greet,
   Blest o'er all other mortals.

3. 'Hail Mary!' quod that Angel mild,
   'Of woman-kind the fairest:
   The Virgin ay shalt thou be styled,
   A babe although thou bearest.'

4. 'How shall I bear a child, that ne'er
   With wedded man was mated?
   Pray tell me now this infant how
   Shall He be generated?'

5. 'O Virgin sheen, it shall be seen,
   As I announce afore thee:
   The Holy Ghost, of virtue most,
   Shall cast his shadow o'er thee.'

6. 'So be it!' God's hand-maiden cried,
   'According to thy telling.'
   Whereon the Angel smartly hied
   Up home-ward to his dwelling.

7. This tiding fill'd his mates with glee:
   'Twas pass'd from one to other,
   That 'twas Marie, and none but she,
   And God would call her Mother.

Holy Week

XXXVIII. THAT VIRGIN'S CHILD

Words by John Gwynneth (*c.* 1530).   Melody and setting by Thomas Tallis (1560).
The Sixth Tune.

1. That Vir-gin's Child, most meek and mild, A - lone - ly for my sake,

His Fa-ther's will for to ful - fil, He came great pains to take.

And suf-fer'd death, as Scrip-ture saith, That we should sa - vèd be,

On Good Fri - day: wherefore I say, He mour - nèd sore for me.

2. Such pain and smart
   As in His heart
       He suffer'd for mankind,
   Can no man take,
   Nor mourning make
       So meekly for his friend.
   The cruel Jews
   Would not refuse
       To nail Him to a tree,
   And with a dart
   To pierce His heart:
       Thus mournèd He for me.

3. Now Christ Jesú,
   Of love most true,
       Have mercy upon me:
   I ask Thee grace
   For my trespass,
       That I have done to Thee.
   For Thy sweet Name,
   Save me from shame
       And all adversitie:
   For Mary's sake,
   To Thee me take,
       And mourn no more for me.

4

XXXIX. JESU, MALTREATED

(O dulcis Jesus)

The Latin words from *Piae Cantiones*, 1582 ; the English words by G. R. W.   The melody also from *Piae Cantiones*, harmonized by G. R. W.

Je - su, mal - treat - ed, rough - ly greet - ed, with re - peat - ed
O   dul - cis Je - sus, spi - nis læ - sus, fla - gris cæ - sus

scoff and blow, O   spare us, young or   hoa - ry! Who foughtest knightly,
a - spe - ris, ve - lis pla - ca - tus   fo - re! Qui lux de lu - ce,

and didst right-ly quell th' un-sight-ly fiend our foe, and now   art clad with
vi - cto du - ce, pen dens cru - ce   sce - le - ris, in - du - tus es splen-

glo - ry. From hell-gate, long their pri - son, Thy people Thou un - chain-est ; And
do - re. In - fer - ni por-tas ur - gens, in - de tu - os du - xi - sti, Post

Thou, the third day ris - - en, as King su - preme re - main - est.
tri - du - um re - sur - - gens, mun - di vi - ctor fu - i - - sti.

XL. WEEP NOT O'ER ME, O MOTHER MINE

Words of Μὴ ἐποδύρου μου, Μῆτερ (Heirmos of Ode IX on Holy Saturday) translated by G. R. W. for the tune of *A the syghes that come fro my herte* (MS. Reg. App. 58, in the time of K. Henry viij), harmonized by C. W.

1. Weep not o'er me, O Mo-ther mine, In grave to see me
2. For in glo - ry I shall a - gen A - rise, as God, and

laid, . . . The well - be - lov - èd Son of thine, Y-
raise . . . To glo - ry faith - ful Chri-sten men, Who

born of Ma - ry e - ver Maid. . . . .
ho - nour thee with love and praise. . . . .

4*

XLI. JEWRY, WHY WITH BULRUSH MOCK HIM?

Words by G. R. W. Tune of *Put the gown upon the bishop*, a very old Scottish sacred melody, in the Mixo-lydian Mode, harmonized by C. W.

1. Jew-ry, why with bul-rush mock Him? Of His own robe why un-frock Him? Thorn-crown'd, why in pur-ple smock Him? Jew-ry, why with bul-rush mock Him? Jew-ry, why with bul-rush mock Him?

2. Though ye clamour, 'Crucify Him,'
   Though ye gainsay, though ye try Him
   In your law-court, and deny Him,
   Though ye clamour, 'Crucify Him.' (ij.)

3. God can be o'ercome by nó man,
   Be it Hebrew, Greek, or Roman.
   Therefore cease to be His foe-man,
   God can be o'ercome by nó man. (ij.)

4. Such as hate Him shall be scatter'd,
   Satan's bolts and bars be batter'd,
   Death and hell-gate throughly shatter'd;
   Such as hate Him shall be scatter'd. (ij.)

Easter=Tide

XLII. O FOR A LAY! FOR ON THIS DAY

Words by G. R. W. Tune, *Mit Freuden zart zu dieser Fahrt* (*Bohemian Brethren*, 1566), harmonized by C. W.

1. O for a lay! For on this day, This day, the first of the se - ven,
Christ is re-stored to life, the Lord, Mon-arch of earth and of hea - ven.

De - feat - ed hell, and death as well, On East - er -

E'en our God is seen Stand-ing a - mid the E - le - ven.

2. Fair was the morn when Christ was born,
   But fairer yet is the morrow,
   When from the dead uprose our Head,
   Ending our night-time of sorrow.
   And from the light of Easter bright
   We, ash and dust, sure hope and trust
   Of our agen-rising borrow.

3. So, man, rejoice, uplift thy voice,
   Alle-Alle-Alleluya.
   Soothly 'tis time to clang the chime,
   Alle-Alle-Alleluya.
   Sirs, pray you, sing to Christ our King,
   Who, lately slain, is ris'n again ;
   Alle-Alle-Alleluya.

XLIII. MOSES, SING UNTO CHRIST THY KING

Words by G. R. W.   Tune of *Old King Cole*, harmonized by C. W.

℣. Mo - ses, sing un - to Christ, thy King, Who hath won the vic - to -

ry, And hath laid low haughty Pha - ra - o Un - der - neath the deep Red

Sea. ℟. Yea, mer-ry, mer-ry, mer-ry, mer-ry, mer-ry may we be, As

bird up-on the ber-ry of the may or cher-ry tree, While as we stand with

harp in hand On the shore of the Red Red Sea.

℣. God perforce overthrew the horse,
    Rider, car, and axle-tree.
  They sank as lead, and their men lie dead,
    Dead as stone: so mote it be!

℟. *Then merry, merry, etc.*

℣. His right hand, and His wonder-wand
    Did divide, at His decree,
  The surging wave, and thereby did save
    Us and ours from slavery.

℟. *Then merry, merry, etc.*

℣. Egypt spake, 'I will overtake
    And despoil mine enemy :
  I will, and must, satisfy my lust
    On the folk of Jewery.'

℟. *But merry, merry, etc.*

℣. Thou didst blow, and entomb our foe
    In the bottom of the sea :
  And, if dry-shod we went o'er, O God,
    Be ascribed the praise to Thee!

℟. *While merry, merry, etc.*

℣. Miriam, wake! Lute and timbrel take !
    With thy women dance for glee !
  And make respond to thy brother yond
    With the Staff, that set us free !

℟. *For merry, merry, etc.*

XLIV. REJOICE, O QUEEN OF BLISS ANON
(After *Regina caeli, letare*)

Words, apparently of the twelfth century, turned into English by G. R. W.
Tune, *Hey the rantin Murray's ha'*, harmonized by G. R. W.

1. Re - joice, O Queen of bliss, a-non: *Hi - la - ri-ter, hi - la - ri - ter.*

Re-joice, thy grief is past and gone. *Hi - la - ri-ter, hi - la - ri - ter.*

2. Abate thy tears, bid woe farewell:
   Hilariter, hilariter,
Thy Son hath harrow'd death and hell.
   Hilariter, hilariter.

3. He, whom thou mournest, Mother-maid,
   Hilariter, hilariter,
Is risen agen, as He fore-said.
   Hilariter, hilariter.

4. The bloody sweat from off His brow,
   Hilariter, hilariter,
Is fraught with healing balsam now.
   Hilariter, hilariter.

5. His visage, marr'd as other none,
   Hilariter, hilariter,
Now beameth brighter than the sun.
   Hilariter, hilariter.

6. His drink of gall and vinegar,
   Hilariter, hilariter,
Than honey-comb is sweeter far.
   Hilariter, hilariter.

7. The scornful Reed, the Lance, the Tree,
   Hilariter, hilariter,
The Victor's Palm and Sceptre be.
   Hilariter, hilariter;

8. His death, in time replete with woe, *Hilariter, hilariter,*
Is glory now for evermo.   *Hilariter, hilariter.*

XLV. THUS ON EASTER-MORROW

Words, English and Latin, by G. R. W.   Tune, *Branle des Sabots*, from Thoinot
Arbeau's *Orchésographie*, Langres (1588), harmonized by C. W.

PART I.

1. Thus on Easter morrow
   Spake an Angel bright and clear :
   ' 'Tis no time for sorrow ;
   Maries, be you of good cheer.
   Christ, arisen from His prison,
   Is not here.

2. Why, as He were mortal,
   Lifeless in the sepulchre,
   Bring ye, to the portal
   Of the empty chamber, myrrh ?
   What befel ye here, go tell ye,
   Nor defer.'

PART II.

1. *Eya ! Resurrexit*
   Jesus Christus hodie ;
   Mala nostra texit :
   Ideo concinite,
   Alleluya, Alleluya,
   Domine.

2. *Resurrexit verè*
   Pro peccante homine :
   Ideo sincerè,
   Christiani, psallite,
   ' Te cantamus, te laudamus,
   Domine.'

XLVI. WITH MELODY, O CHRIST, HYMN WE

Words by G. R. W. Tune, the close of *Christ ist erstanden* (twelfth century,
or earlier), harmonized by J. S. Bach (1685-1750).

With me - lo - dy, O Christ, hymn we Thy vic - to - ry. As

this day saw Thee win it, We will be joy - ful

Al - - - le - lu - - - i - a

in . . . it. Al - - - - le - lu - i - a.

XLVII. NIGHTINGALE, THY LORDLY LAYS
(*Nachtigall, dein edler Schall*)

Translated by G. R. W. from D. G. Corner, 1625 ; harmonized by C. W.

Night - in - gale, thy lord - ly lays   Tell the hea - vy - heart - ed
Of   re - turn - ing sum - mer days,   Win - ter-gloom de - part - ed:

At   thy   mu - sick thorn and thatch   Stand with rap - ture smit - ten :

On   my   song - ster roll thy match   Still re - mains un - writ - ten.

XLVIII. WHEN THE EARTH, WITH SPRING RETURNING
(*Cum telluris vere novo*)

Words by St. Fulbert, Bishop of Chartres († 1028), translated by J. M. Neale (1818-1866). Melody of *Mos florentis venustatis*, from a *Mosburg Gradual* (1360), harmonized by C. W.

1. When the earth, with Spring re-turn-ing, vests her-self in fresh-er sheen,
   And the glades and lea-fy thick-ets are ar-ray'd in liv-ing green;
   When a sweet-er fra-grance breath-eth flow-'ry fields and vales a-long,
   Then, tri-um-phant in her glad-ness, Phi-lo-mel be-gins her song.

2. And with thick delicious warble far and wide her notes she flings,
   Telling of the happy Spring-tide, and the joys that summer brings.
   In the pauses of men's slumber deep and full she pours her voice:
   In the labour of his travel bids the wayfarer rejoice.

3. Night and day, from bush and greenwood, sweeter than an earthly lyre,
   She, unwearied songstress, carols, distancing the feath'red quire;
   In her airy flight ascending to the summit of the tree,
   Thence full fain she trills her mellow canticles of festal glee,

4. Fills the hill-side, fills the valley, bids the groves and thickets ring,
   Made indeed exceeding glorious thro' the joyousness of Spring.
   None could teach such heav'nly music, none implant such tuneful skill,
   Save the King of realms celestial, who doth all things as He will.

On Trinity Sunday and at Other Times

XLIX. 'TWAS IN THE YEAR THAT KING UZZIAH DIED

A metrical version by G. R. W. of Isaiah vi. 1–4. The tune, in the Fifth Mode, is a metrical form of the *Sanctus* (this certainly not later than the tenth century) which used to be sung, according to Salisbury Use, on Sundays and Simple Feasts of the second and third class, and throughout Octaves, *cum regimine chori*. The setting, with a few alterations, is of the early sixteenth century, and is taken from Layriz (*Jesaja dem profeten das geschah*).

'Twas in the year that King Uz-zi-ah died, A vi-sion
by I-sai-ah was a-spied: A lof-ty throne—The Lord was
set there-on; And with His glo-ry all the tem-ple shone.
Bright Se-ra-phim were stand-ing round a-bout. Six wings had

eve - ry of that quire de - vout. With twain he awe - some veil'd his

face, and so With twain he dread - ful veil'd his feet be - low,

With twain did he now hi - ther, thi - ther fly: And thus a -

loud did one to o - ther cry: 'Ho - ly is God, the Lord of

Sa - ba - oth: Ho - ly is God, the Lord of Sa - ba - oth,

Ho - ly is God, the Lord of Sa - ba - oth, Full of His

glory are earth and hea - ven, both.' And at their cry the lin - tels

moved a - pace, And clouds of in - cense fill'd the Ho - ly Place.

L. I WAS, AND AM, AND AY SHALL BE
SAD-HEARTED

Words by G. R. W. Tune, *Ic seg adieu*, a Dutch melody of 1602, harmonized by C. W.

I was, and am, And ay shall be sad - heart - - -

ed For Wal - sing - ham, To see her day de - part - - -

ed: Her min-ster walls and stalls o'er- Her cells and wells with moss o'er- A-bove her
thrown,　　　　　　　grown:

own, were stood the throne Of　Ma - ry's Son, Lo! now ne'er a stone.

LI. A SONG FOR THE TIMES

Words by J. M. Neale.   Tune, *Prince Rupert's March* (early seventeenth century),
harmonized by C. W.

1. A Song for the times when the sweet bright Church chimes Call'd
   As they open'd their eyes by the bright sun - rise, And when

rich and poor to pray,
eve - ning died a - way: The Squire came out of his

rich old hall, And the pea - sants two and by . . three;   The

wood-man let his hat - chet fall, And the shep - herd left his tree.

* Here and elsewhere (to accommodate the words) a crotchet will have to be split up
into two quavers.

2. Through the Churchyard dew, by the Churchyard yew,
   They went, both old and young,
And with one consent in prayer they bent,
   And with one consent they sung.
They knelt on the floor till the prayers were o'er ;
   To the priest they gave good heed :
Who would not praise those good old days,
   When the Church was a Church indeed ?

3. Christmas was merry Christmas then,
   And Easter-tide the same :
And they welcomed well with merry bell
   Each Saint's day as it came.
They thought with love on the Saints above
   In the pious days of old :
We toil and we slave till we drop in the grave,
   And all for the lust of gold.

4. But little we'll care what wicked men
   May say or think, of ill,
They kept the Saints' days holy then,
   We'll keep them holy still.
We'll cherish them now in times of strife,
   As a holy and peaceful thing ;
They were bought by a faithful Prelate's life,*
   And the blood of a martyr'd king.†

      * William Laud, Archbishop and Martyr.
      † King Charles the First.

LII. SUMMER IS BANISH'D

(*Loybere risen*)

A Minnesänger Song by Wizlab (of the thirteenth century). Englished and harmonized by C. R. W.

Sum-mer is ba-nish'd; Late the sun ris-eth, heigh-o!.... And

ne'er flow'r spring-eth: Green leaf is va-nish'd:

Now by our hedge and wood-row... No night-in-gale

sing-eth, But o'er lea and moun-tain Bo-re-as' bu-gle doth

blow, Be - numb - ing all, cat - tle and dro - ver,

Freez - ing the foun - tain, Mant - ling the mea - dow with

snow. . Ay me! for glad sum - mer is o - ver.

LIII. ZACCHAEUS CLIMBS A TREE
(*Zacchaeus arboris*)

Words translated by G. R. W. from *Piae cantiones* (1582), whence also the musical setting.

1. Zac - chae - us climbs a tree, a sy - - co - more it is, To catch a glimpse of Christ, the King of heav'n - ly bliss.

2. When Jesus pass'd the place, He lift His blessèd eyes,
   And to Zacchaeus gave commandment on this wise :

3. 'Zacchaeus, haste thee down, and hither to My side !
   For at thy house to-day I must with thee abide.'

4. Then did Zacchaeus make our Lord a welcome guest,
   And entertain'd Him well, not sparing of his best :

5. The chamber of his heart he oped, and said moreo'er,
   'Where I have wrongèd man, there four-fold I restore :

6. 'With half-part of my goods the beggar's want I ease.'
   God loveth well such faith, and works, the like of these.

7. Then merry make we, for the Feast requires it so :
   Benédicámus Dóminórum Dómino !

8. So praise the Three in One ! and after time of Mass,
   Deó dicámus infinitas gracias !

PRINTED IN GREAT BRITAIN BY
BILLING AND SONS LIMITED, GUILDFORD AND LONDON
H4857